THIS IS MY STORY

by _____

begun on _____

Memories fill my mind—
of people I have loved, places I have known,
moments I have cherished.
These are personal riches,
treasures from
my heart.

For our parents.

Special thanks to Gail Levites, Peter Neumann, and Pat Upton.

Published by The C.R. Gibson Company, 32 Knight Street, Norwalk,
Connecticut 06856.

ISBN 0-8378-9272-4

Printed in USA

SWEET MEMORIES

A WOMAN'S JOURNAL

Created, written, and designed by
CYNTHIA HART and LEONARD TODD

C O N T

MY CHILDHOOD

A time when everything is a discovery: the comforting touch of a teddy bear or the far glimmer of a star. Where arms won't reach, dreams will.

GROWING UP

No longer a child, not quite an adult. Life brims with feelings never encountered before!

ON MY WAY

Stepping out into the world: an exhilerating event, whether it means traveling away to college or beginning a career. New horizons ahead!

ROMANTIC NOTIONS

The realm of feelings: where attractions and fascinations rule the heart and defy reason.

A LIFE TOGETHER

Two people: caring for each other, exploring what really matters, weathering the ups and downs.

MOTHERHOOD

Bringing a new generation into the world: an affirmation of hope, an adventure full of surprises.

MY FAMILY

Family memories are taken for granted until one day they slip away. Here, a permanent record.

E   N   T   S

MILESTONES

Contrasting moments of happiness and sadness, moments that change our lives. Each is a milestone and a source of new strength.

FRIENDS AND OTHER PLEASURES

Close friends, special places, favorite things: some of the pieces that come together to make a happy life.

SHEER MADNESS

Irresistible temptations known to every woman: moments when reason disappears and madness reigns.

THE WORLD AROUND ME

A life is shaped by many influences; not the least of these are great world events. In this section, history as I saw it.

SELF-PORTRAIT

One year builds on another: choices become clearer, goals are more nearly within reach. The future beckons!

MY CHILDHOOD

A time when everything is a discovery:
the comforting touch of a teddy bear
or the far glimmer of a star.
Where arms won't reach,
dreams will.

 was born on _____

I was named _____

_____

My parents have told me that as a baby I _____

_____

_____

_____

*M*y earliest memory is

_____
_____
_____
_____
_____
_____
_____

I remember my father as _____
_____
_____

I remember my mother as _____
_____
_____

Other people were important to me too. I especially recall _____
_____
_____
_____
_____

The home I grew up in was _____

_____

My favorite toys were _____

_____

My favorite games were _____

_____

My favorite pets were _____

_____

I liked to pretend that I _____

_____

_____

_____

_____

When I grew up, I wanted to be _____

_____

_____

SCHOOL DAYS

On my first day of school, I _____

_____

_____

_____

_____

The best part of school was _____

_____

_____

_____

_____

My favorite teachers were _____

_____

_____

_____

My best friends were _____

_____

_____

_____

_____

_____

_____

_____

_____

_____

After school, we liked to _____

_____

_____

_____

_____

_____

_____

_____

_____

My most exciting childhood adventure was _____

_____

_____

_____

_____

_____

_____

_____

_____

_____

_____

_____

_____

My favorite family vacations were _____

_____

M*y best childhood memories are*

_____

My worst childhood memories are _____

*W*hen I look back on my childhood, I remember it as

_____

_____

_____

_____

_____

_____

_____

At night when I wished upon a star, I wished _____

_____

_____

Other thoughts about my childhood _____

_____

_____

_____

_____

_____

_____

_____

GROWING
UP

No longer a child, not quite an adult.
Life brims with feelings never
encountered before!

A teenager at last! The best part of being grown up was

_____

_____

_____

_____

_____

On the other hand, I had trouble with _____

_____

_____

_____

_____

_____

My relationship with my parents was _____

_____

_____

_____

_____

_____

_____

_____

_____

_____

We disagreed about _____

_____

_____

_____

_____

_____

*igh school was a completely new experience for me—
new teachers, new friends, new lessons to be learned
about life.*

My favorite teachers were _____

_____

_____

_____

_____

They inspired me to _____

_____

_____

_____

_____

_____

_____

The subjects I liked best were _____

_____

_____

_____

_____

_____

The subjects I found most difficult were _____

_____

_____

_____

_____

_____

My grades were _____

_____

_____

_____

_____

_____

_____

The sports and extracurricular activities I participated in were _____

_____

_____

_____

_____

_____

_____

_____

*S*ome of my best friends during high school were

_____

_____

_____

_____

When I went out with my friends, we liked to _____

_____

_____

_____

_____

_____

I learned to drive a car by _____

_____

_____

_____

The day I got my license, I _____

_____

_____

_____

How did I look as a teenager?

_____

_____

_____

_____

_____

_____

_____

_____

M*y body went through amazing changes. I remember*_____

_____

_____

_____

_____

_____

_____

_____

_____

_____

_____

_____

Wearing make-up and high heels was exciting. I especially enjoyed

_____

_____

_____

_____

_____

_____

_____

_____

_____

_____

_____

T*he fashions and fads I followed were* _____

_____

_____

_____

_____

_____

_____

_____

THE OPPOSITE SEX

Boys began to interest me. I thought they were

_____

_____

_____

_____

_____

The first boy I had a crush on was _____

_____

_____

_____

_____

_____

_____

I thought he was wonderful because _____

_____

_____

_____

_____

He thought I was _____

_____

_____

I remember my first date _____

_____

_____

_____

_____

_____

_____

_____

I especially remember my first kiss _____

_____

_____

_____

_____

_____

_____

My first real boyfriend was _____

_____

_____

Memories of my senior prom _____

_____

_____

_____

High school graduation was a momentous occasion.
To me it meant _____

_____

_____

_____

In the yearbook it said that I was _____

_____

_____

_____

O ther teenage memories to cherish _____

_____

_____

_____

_____

_____

TEENAGE FAVORITES

Musical groups _____

_____

_____

_____

Singers _____

_____

_____

_____

_____

Songs _____

_____

_____

_____

_____

Movies _____

_____

_____

_____

Actors _____

_____

_____

_____

Books _____

_____

_____

_____

_____

Television or radio shows _____

_____

_____

_____

_____

Athletes _____

_____

_____

_____

Dances _____

_____

_____

_____

Clothes _____

_____

_____

_____

ON MY WAY

Stepping out into the world:
an exhilarating event, whether it
means traveling away to college
or beginning a career.
New horizons ahead!

After high school, I had many choices to make. I decided

_____

_____

_____

_____

_____

_____

My ambition was _____

_____

_____

_____

_____

How did I feel about going out into the world? _____

_____

_____

_____

_____

_____

The people who influenced me the most at this time were _____

_____

_____

_____

_____

_____

COLLEGE

The school I attended was _____

_____

_____

I was there from _____ to _____ , Class of_____

_____

The degree I received was _____

_____

_____

My major subject of study was _____

_____

_____

_____

Teachers who influenced me were _____

_____

_____

_____

My roommates were _____

_____

_____

_____

_____

My closest friends were _____

_____

_____

_____

_____

_____

My social life at college was _____

_____

_____

_____

_____

_____

_____

_____

During my vacations I _____

_____

_____

_____

_____

My greatest challenge in college was _____

_____

_____

_____

_____

For me, college graduation was _____

_____

_____

_____

_____

_____

_____

_____

The most important benefits of college were _____

_____

_____

_____

_____

_____

My fondest memories of college are _____

_____

_____

_____

_____

_____

_____

_____

_____

_____

After college I hoped to _____

_____

_____

_____

_____

CAREER

I went to work when I was _____

_____

My job was _____

_____

_____

_____

_____

_____

_____

_____

A place of my own? I decided to live _____

_____

_____

_____

_____

_____

How did I manage my finances? _____

_____

_____

_____

_____

My new life had pluses and minuses. The negative side was _____

The positive side was _____

Career moves which followed _____

_____

_____

_____

_____

W*as I pleased with my job choices?*

_____

_____

_____

_____

_____

As I progressed in my career, I learned _____

_____

_____

_____

_____

_____

_____

The most enjoyable aspects of my work _____

_____

_____

_____

_____

_____

_____

_____

_____

_____

_____

*M*ore career history _____

_____

_____

_____

_____

_____

_____

ROMANTIC
NOTIONS

The realm of feelings:
where attractions and fascinations
rule the heart and defy reason.

When I was younger, I expected love to _____

_____

_____

_____

_____

I was most intrigued by men who _____

_____

_____

_____

_____

_____

_____

_____

Now, what I want most from a man is _____

_____

_____

_____

_____

_____

In return, I'd like to give him _____

_____

_____

_____

_____

I feel especially romantic when

_____

_____

_____

_____

_____

_____

_____

_____

My most pleasurable romantic fantasies are _____

_____

_____

_____

_____

_____

_____

_____

_____

_____

_____

For me, sexuality is _____

_____

_____

Finding the right man isn't easy! My favorite schemes _____

_____

_____

_____

_____

_____

_____

_____

_____

Blind dates can be quite a surprise. I'll always remember_____

_____

_____

_____

_____

Did I ever experience love at first sight?

_____

_____

_____

_____

_____

A *man I can't forget*

*W*hen my heart was broken,

I recovered by _____

_____

_____

_____

_____

_____

_____

_____

_____

_____

I've learned from love that _____

_____

_____

_____

_____

_____

_____

_____

_____

_____

_____

More about romance

A
LIFE
TOGETHER

Two people:
caring for each other,
exploring what really matters,
weathering the ups and downs.

To me, truly falling in love means _____

_____

_____

_____

_____

I knew I had found the right man for me when I met _____

_____

_____

_____

_____

_____

_____

I was especially attracted to him because _____

_____

_____

_____

_____

_____

He was attracted to me because _____

_____

_____

_____

_____

_____

COURTSHIP

*O*n our first date we _____

_____

_____

_____

_____

_____

_____

*O*ur first kiss was _____

_____

_____

_____

_____

_____

A very special evening _____

_____

_____

_____

_____

We wanted to marry because _____

_____

_____

_____

_____

_____

_____

_____

_____

We became engaged _____

_____

How did our families react? _____

_____

_____

_____

_____

_____

MARRIAGE

We were married on _____

_____

On my wedding day, I felt _____

_____
_____
_____
_____
_____

My most vivid memories of our wedding are _____

_____
_____
_____
_____
_____
_____
_____
_____
_____
_____
_____

On our honeymoon, we _____

_____

_____

_____

_____

_____

_____

_____

_____

_____

Our first home was _____

_____

_____

_____

_____

As we began our life together, our hopes and dreams _____

_____

_____

_____

_____

_____

Our greatest accomplishments _____

_____

_____

_____

_____

_____

_____

_____

_____

Our mutual interests _____

_____

_____

_____

_____

_____

_____

_____

_____

_____

_____

_____

Our areas of disagreement _____

_____

_____

_____

_____

_____

_____

H*ave we ever considered separating?* _____

_____

_____

_____

_____

To make our relationship work, we _____

_____

_____

_____

_____

_____

Has marriage lived up to my expectations?

The most important lesson I've learned about marriage is _____

Hopes for our life together in the future

MOTHERHOOD

Bringing a new generation into the world:
an affirmation of hope,
an adventure full of surprises.

When I thought about having children, I imagined _____

_____

_____

_____

A*fter I found out I was going to have my first baby, I* _____

_____

_____

_____

_____

_____

_____

_____

Daddy-To-Be felt _____

_____

_____

_____

_____

_____

_____

_____

_____

_____

_____

I remember pregnancy as _____

_____

_____

_____

_____

_____

_____

_____

_____

For me, giving birth was _____

_____

_____

_____

_____

_____

_____

_____

_____

_____

*In what ways did becoming a mother change my life?*_____

_____

_____

_____

_____

_____

_____

_____

_____

_____

_____

_____

*How did it affect my career?*_____

_____

_____

_____

_____

_____

_____

_____

MY CHILDREN

My children's names and birthdates are

_____
_____
_____
_____
_____
_____
_____
_____
_____
_____
_____
_____
_____

Memories about each child _____

_____
_____
_____
_____
_____
_____

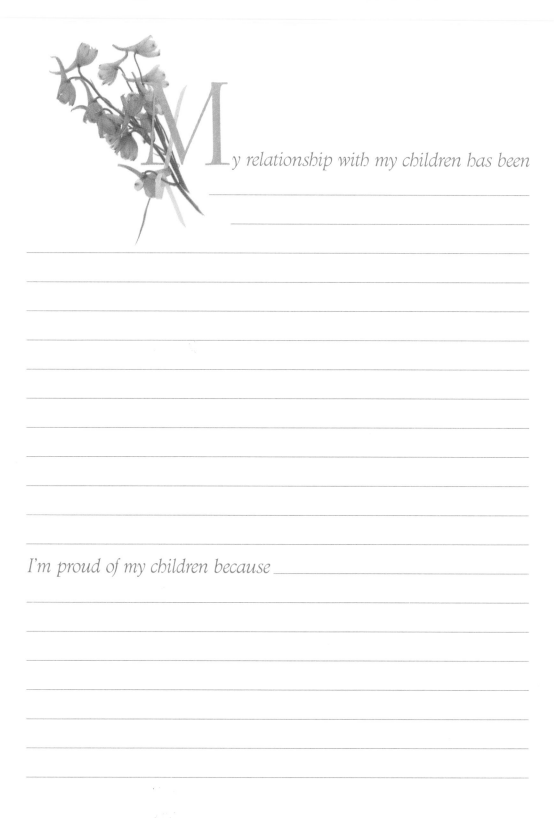

y relationship with my children has been

_____

_____

_____

_____

_____

_____

_____

_____

_____

_____

_____

I'm proud of my children because _____

_____

_____

_____

_____

_____

_____

_____

I have learned from my children that _____

_____

_____

_____

_____

_____

_____

_____

_____

_____

Ｈow do I feel about becoming a grandmother?

_____

_____

_____

_____

_____

_____

_____

_____

O*ther joys of motherhood* _____

_____

MY FAMILY

Family memories are taken for granted
until one day they slip away.
Here, a permanent record.

My happiest memories of my mother are _____

_____

_____

_____

_____

_____

_____

Her most endearing qualities

From her I inherited my

One of the funniest things my mother ever said to me was _____

_____

_____

_____

_____

_____

T*he most important advice my mother gave me was*

_____

_____

_____

_____

_____

_____

_____

_____

_____

_____

_____

*M*y happiest memories of my father

_____

_____

_____

_____

_____

_____

_____

_____

_____

_____

His most endearing qualities _____

_____

_____

_____

_____

_____

_____

From him I inherited my _____

_____

_____

_____

_____

One of the funniest things my father ever said to me was _____

_____

_____

_____

_____

The most important advice my father gave me was _____

_____

_____

_____

_____

He always encouraged me to _____

_____

_____

_____

_____

_____

A grandparent's love can span generations.
My fondest memories of my mother's parents are

My fondest memories of my father's parents are _____

_____

_____

_____

_____

_____

_____

_____

_____

_____

_____

_____

_____

_____

_____

_____

_____

_____

_____

_____

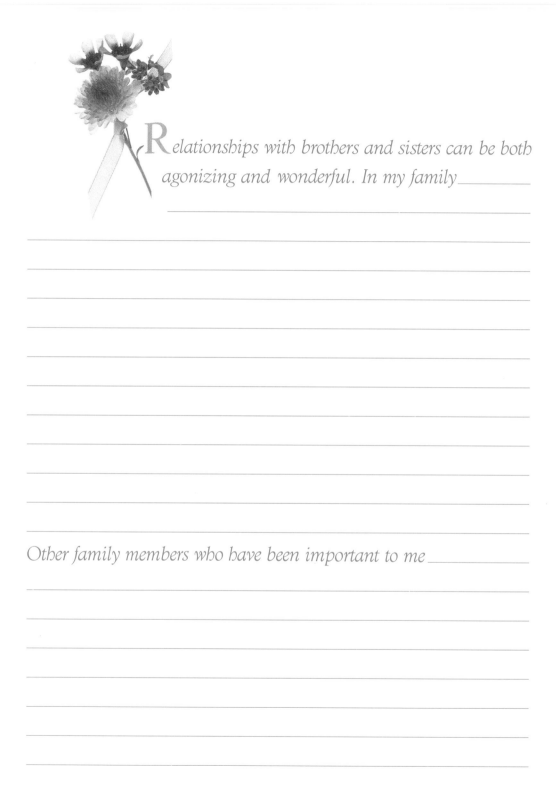

Relationships with brothers and sisters can be both agonizing and wonderful. In my family _____

_____

_____

_____

_____

_____

_____

_____

_____

_____

_____

_____

_____

Other family members who have been important to me _____

_____

_____

_____

_____

_____

_____

_____

Many of our family rituals and customs revolve around holidays. I especially enjoy _____

_____

_____

_____

_____

_____

_____

_____

_____

E *nduring family legends maintain that* _____

_____

_____

_____

_____

_____

_____

_____

_____

_____

A FAMILY HISTORY

My mother's maiden name _____

She was born in _____ *on* _____

Her brothers' and sisters' names _____

_____

_____

She went to school at _____

_____

After she finished school, she _____

_____

_____

_____

My father's name _____

He was born in _____ *on* _____

His brothers' and sisters' names _____

_____

_____

He went to school at _____

_____

After he finished school, he _____

_____

_____

My parents met when _____

_____

_____

_____

They were married in _____ *on* _____

They lived in _____

_____

_____

_____

I was their _____ *child born on* _____ *at* _____

The place of my birth was _____

_____

M*y brothers' and sisters' names and birthdates*

_____

_____

_____

_____

_____

_____

_____

_____

Mother's Family

My grandmother's maiden name _____

_____

Her parents' names _____

_____

They came from _____

_____

_____

_____

My grandfather's name _____

His parents' names _____

_____

They came from _____

_____

_____

_____

My grandparents were married in _____

on _____

They settled in _____

_____

_____

_____

In stories about my mother's family, I've been told that

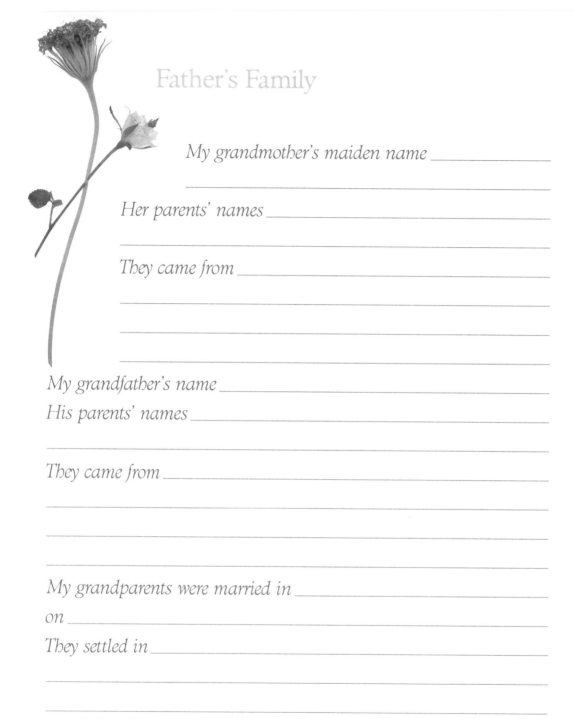

Father's Family

My grandmother's maiden name _____

_____

Her parents' names _____

_____

They came from _____

_____

_____

_____

My grandfather's name _____

His parents' names _____

_____

They came from _____

_____

_____

_____

My grandparents were married in _____

on _____

They settled in _____

_____

_____

_____

In stories about my father's family, I've been told that

*O*ther family remembrances _____

MILESTONES

Contrasting moments of happiness and sadness,
moments that change our lives.
Each is a milestone and a
source of new strength.

The greatest joys of my life have been _____

_____

_____

_____

_____

The accomplishments I'm most happy about are _____

_____

_____

_____

_____

_____

_____

_____

_____

_____

_____

_____

_____

_____

Sometimes I had to fight for what I believed in.
A battle I'm still proud of is _____

_____

_____

_____

_____

The greatest sorrows of my life _____

_____

_____

_____

_____

My most trusted help in those times _____

_____

_____

_____

_____

_____

_____

I *was able to overcome my sadness by*

_____

_____

_____

_____

_____

_____

From my joys and sorrows, I have learned _____

_____

_____

_____

_____

_____

_____

Now, I try to live each day _____

_____

_____

_____

_____

_____

_____

_____

_____

_____

_____

_____

_____

My most deeply held beliefs are _____

_____

_____

_____

_____

_____

_____

_____

_____

_____

_____

_____

_____

_____

_____

_____

_____

_____

_____

_____

_____

_____

_____

_____

FRIENDS
AND OTHER PLEASURES

Close friends, special places, favorite things:
some of the pieces that come together
to make a happy life.

As I grow older, I value friendship more and more.

To me, it means _____

_____

_____

_____

Friendships must be nurtured. With my friends I try to _____

_____

_____

_____

_____

_____

_____

What do I want from them in return?_____

_____

_____

_____

_____

_____

_____

Have I ever had to call on my friends for help?_____

_____

_____

_____

_____

_____

FAVORITE PEOPLE

Over the years I have built many wonderful and lasting relationships. These are some of the ones I cherish most:

My friend's name _____

We met when _____

_____

This friendship is important to me because _____

_____

I especially remember the time when _____

_____

_____

_____

My friend's name _____

We met when _____

_____

This friendship is important to me because _____

_____

I especially remember the time when _____

_____

_____

_____

My friend's name _____

We met when _____

_____

_____

This friendship is important to me because _____

_____

_____

I especially remember the time when _____

_____

_____

My friend's name _____

We met when _____

_____

_____

This friendship is important to me because _____

_____

I especially remember the time when _____

_____

_____

_____

My friend's name _____

We met when _____

_____

_____

This friendship is important to me because _____

_____

_____

I especially remember the time when _____

_____

_____

_____

My friend's name _____

We met when _____

_____

_____

This friendship is important to me because

_____

_____

I especially remember the time when

_____

_____

_____

M y friend's name _____

We met when _____

_____

_____

This friendship is important to me because _____

_____

_____

I especially remember the time when _____

_____

_____

M y friend's name _____

We met when _____

_____

_____

This friendship is important to me because

_____

_____

I especially remember the time when _____

_____

_____

*M*ore friends

FAVORITE PLACES

Places have personalities just as people do. Of all the places I've lived, I was fondest of_____

_____

_____

_____

_____

_____

_____

_____

_____

_____

_____

In my travels, the places I enjoyed most were _____

_____

_____

_____

_____

_____

_____

One day I'd like to visit _____

_____

_____

_____

_____

_____

_____

_____

_____

_____

_____

_____

_____

_____

_____

_____

_____

_____

_____

_____

_____

_____

_____

FAVORITE THINGS

Here are my personal favorites and the
reasons why I love them:

Flowers _____

_____

_____

Fragrances _____

_____

_____

Music _____

_____

_____

Foods _____

_____

_____

Fashions _____

_____

_____

Sports _____

_____

_____

Colors _____

_____

Authors _____

_____

_____

_____

Books _____

_____

_____

_____

Plays _____

_____

_____

_____

Movies _____

_____

_____

_____

Artists _____

_____

_____

Works of art _____

_____

_____

Personal collections _____

_____

_____

_____

O*ther favorites* _____

_____

_____

_____

_____

_____

_____

_____

_____

_____

_____

_____

_____

SHEER MADNESS

Irresistible temptations known to every woman:
moments when reason disappears
and madness reigns.

Temptations? I'm likely to throw caution to the wind when

_____

_____

_____

The single craziest thing I ever did was _____

_____

_____

_____

_____

_____

_____

_____

_____

_____

_____

_____

When I crave new experiences, I _____

_____

_____

_____

_____

_____

_____

_____

_____

My most exotic indulgence is _____

_____

_____

_____

_____

_____

_____

My deepest passions are _____

_____

_____

_____

_____

_____

_____

When I go on a spending spree, I _____

_____

_____

_____

_____

What angers me most? _____

_____

_____

_____

_____

_____

T*o let off steam when I'm angry, I* _____

_____

_____

_____

_____

What makes me laugh most? _____

_____

_____

_____

_____

_____

_____

What moves me to tears?

_____

_____

_____

_____

_____

_____

_____

_____

_____

More madness

_____

_____

_____

_____

_____

_____

_____

_____

_____

THREE WISHES

If I were granted three extravagant wishes,
I would ask for:

1 _____

_____

_____

_____

_____

2 _____

_____

_____

_____

_____

_____

3 _____

_____

_____

_____

_____

_____

THE
WORLD
AROUND ME

A life is shaped by many influences;
not the least of these are
great world events. In this section,
history as I saw it.

During my lifetime, I have witnessed these historic events:

Around the world _____

_____

_____

In this country

Here at home

The event that most affected me personally was _____

_____

_____

_____

_____

Because of it, I felt _____

_____

_____

_____

_____

_____

I was also deeply moved by_____

_____

_____

_____

_____

_____

_____   _____

_____

_____

The women and men I most admire are _____

_____

_____

_____

_____

_____

_____

_____

_____

_____

_____

Technological advances that have altered my life _____

_____

_____

_____

_____

_____

_____

_____

_____

*How do I feel about politics?*_____

_____

_____

_____

_____

_____

_____

_____

I have seen the world changed by social movements, such as _____

_____

_____

_____

_____

_____

_____

_____

cause that I championed was

_____

_____

_____

_____

_____

I perceive the world around me today as

My hopes for future world changes

SELF-PORTRAIT

One year builds on another:
choices become clearer, goals are
more nearly within reach.
The future beckons!

As I write these memoirs, I am _____ years old.

At this point in my life, I would describe my best qualities as _____

_____

_____

_____

_____

On the other hand, I'd like to improve _____

_____

_____

_____

_____

_____

_____

_____

_____

_____

_____

Today when I look in the mirror, I see _____

_____

_____

_____

_____

_____

_____

I wish I were _____

_____

_____

_____

_____

My health is _____

_____

_____

_____

_____

_____

_____

I take care of myself by _____

_____

_____

_____

_____

How do I feel about growing older? _____

_____

_____

_____

_____

_____

_____

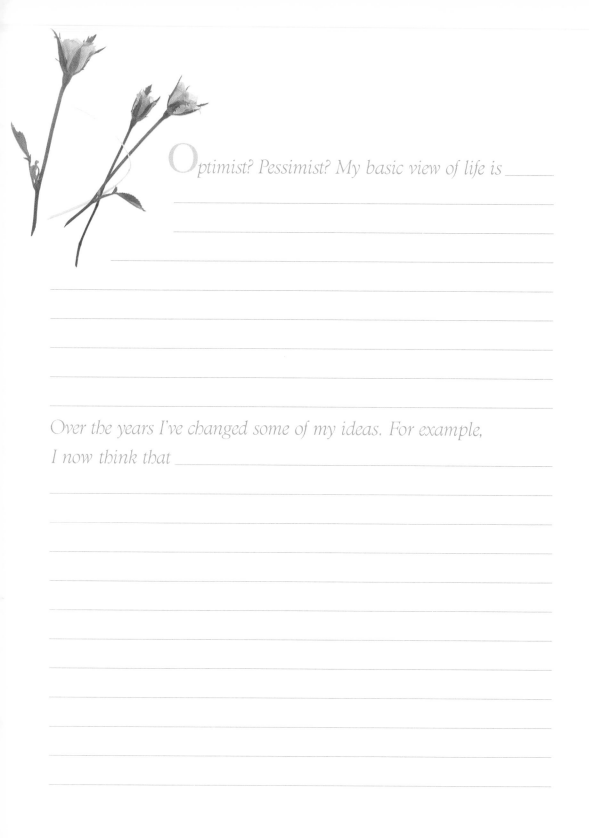

Optimist? Pessimist? My basic view of life is _____

_____

_____

_____

_____

_____

_____

_____

Over the years I've changed some of my ideas. For example,
I now think that _____

_____

_____

_____

_____

_____

_____

_____

_____

_____

_____

Have I reached my goals so far?

The one thing I need in my life more than anything else is

THE FUTURE

There are many directions in which I can steer my life.
This is what I wish to accomplish:
Next month _____

_____

_____

_____

_____

_____

Next year _____

_____

_____

_____

_____

_____

_____

Five years from now _____

_____

_____

_____

_____

_____

_____

*What risks am I willing to take to achieve these goals?*_____

_____

_____

_____

_____

_____

As I look toward the future, I feel _____

_____

_____

_____

_____

_____

_____

_____

_____

_____

_____

_____

_____

_____

My wish for those who read my story

These memoirs
were completed on

_____

by _____